The Great Safe Blag

Jean Ure & Leonard Gregory

Illustrated by
Terry McKenna

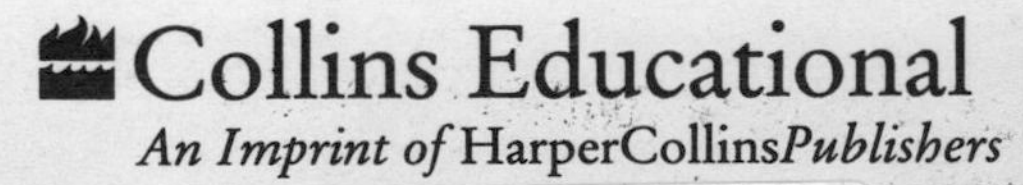

Published by Collins Educational
77-85 Fulham Palace Road, London W6 8JB

ISBN 0 00 323062 7

Illustration, page layout and cover illustration by Terry McKenna.
Cover design by Clinton Banbury.

Commissioning Editor: Domenica de Rosa
Editor: Paula Hammond
Production: Susan Cashin

Typeset by Harper Phototypesetters Ltd, Northampton, England
Printed by Caledonian International, Glasgow, Scotland

The Great Safe Blag

Contents

Chapter 1
Durkin the Gherkin

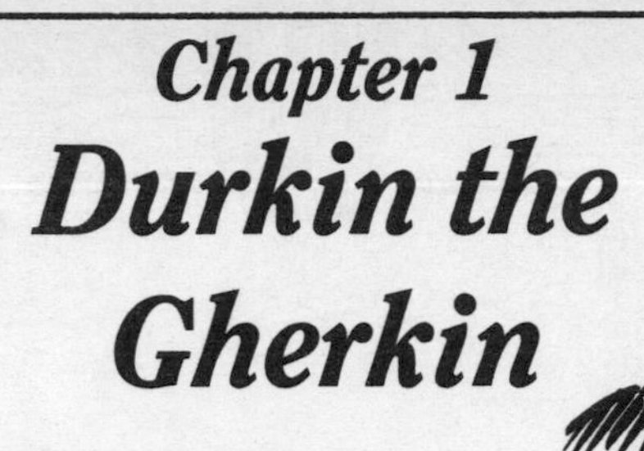

This is Detective Sergeant Clive Durkin (otherwise known as the Lead Truncheon).

Durkin is a hard man. He walks tall and casts a long shadow.

At least, he likes to think he does.

Sometimes, on the street, he's known as "Durkin the Gherkin".

Durkin is attached to the Catford nick.

This is Detective Constable Malcolm Swales (otherwise known as "Malc").

Malc is new to the job. He's going to work with Durkin. What a lucky man!

I'm a hard man, Malc, hard but fair. I walk t-

- all and shoot straight from the hip.

My presence alone can clear streets. I am the law: they will obey. Any questions?
What about public relations?

I never bother about that, and I suggest you don't either. They're scum out there, Malc...scum!

This is the Desk
Sergeant Eric Slocum
(otherwise known as
"Surprise-me-Slocum").

Sergeant, I want to report something!
Go on, surprise me!

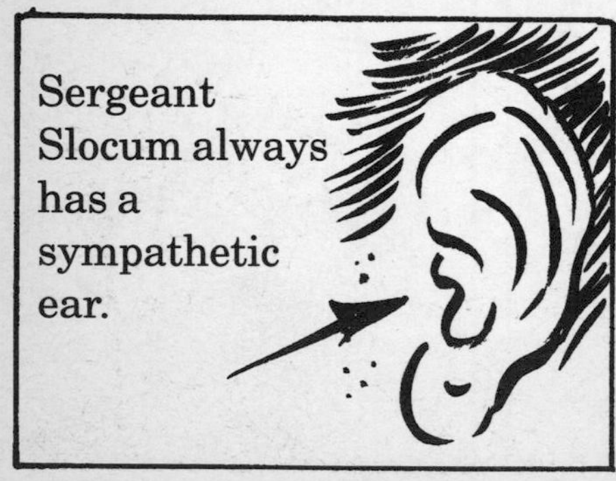
Sergeant
Slocum always
has a
sympathetic
ear.

Someone's stolen my cat!

This is Detective Inspector Phyllis Cracknell (otherwise known as "Ma'am").

Mug shot.

And this is Chief Superintendent Wally Frobisher (otherwise known as "What-a-Wally").

Who's going to be 'mother' today then, Wally?
I poured yesterday, Phyllis. It's your turn today.

I do love a good cup of coffee. It's so much nicer than the stuff out of the machine.

I couldn't agree more, Phyllis. That machine's been a great disappointment to me, I can tell you.

They've not been putting foreign coins in there again have they? I did ask them not to. Oh, they are naughty boys!

PLEASE DO NOT PUT FOREIGN COINS IN THIS MACHINE.
DRINK
FEE – WHITE
FE – BLACK
– SUGAR
I always carry a supply of French francs.

Chapter 2
The Great Safe Blag

Wally and Ma'am are drinking coffee together. They always enjoy a nice cup of coffee round about eleven o'clock. Today, Wally is being mother.

"More French francs in the coffee machine," he says.

"Oh, really!" says Ma'am. "This is too bad!"

"Well, I suppose lads will be lads," says Wally. "Mind you, it is very good for my foreign coin collection."

Ma'am picks up her knitting needles and knits busily.

"That's not the point, Wally. This is a police station; we're supposed to set an example. I shall have to have another word with them."

"If you would, Phyllis; I should be grateful. In the meantime, what are we going to do about these safe robberies?"

“...twenty-one, twenty-two, twenty-three...” Ma’am is counting stitches. “Sorry, dear? What did you say?”

“It’s these safe robberies, Phyllis. There was another one last night. Really, it’s getting beyond a joke! I had the Commissioner on the phone just a few minutes ago. I didn’t know what to tell him. He was very sharp; it quite upset me. He kept shouting things like, ‘You’d better get your act together’ and ‘what the hell is going on in your manor?’ It was most distressing. It’s given me rather a headache.”

There, there! Don't take on so.
By the way, Phyllis...what is going on in my manor?

“Knit one, purl one,” says Ma’am, going back to her knitting. She is making a long stripy scarf for her favourite police informer, Graham O’Grady (otherwise known as “O’Grady-the-Grass”).

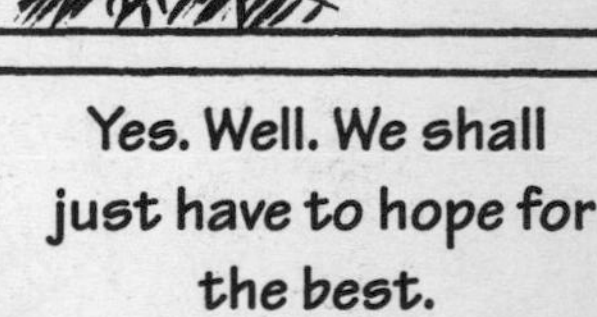

Wally does not sound very optimistic.

Ah! Swiss francs.
They'll do the job.

PLEASE DO NOT
PUT FOREIGN
COINS IN THIS
MACHINE.

TO-DRINK

Chapter 3
Nimble Fingers

So, this is the safe?
Yes. That's the one they left behind. I'm afraid they took the other one with them.

Did they? Did they indeed? Of course, we have only your word for that.

All right, then, let's have a look.

It's empty!
Yes, they took everything, Sergeant.

So you say. Of course, we shall need a statement. You realise that?
Oh, well, yes of course, Sergeant.

"I'll tell you one thing," says Durkin.

"Yes? Yes?" The jeweller says it eagerly. Has the Detective Sergeant found a lead already?

"They done a neat job!" says Durkin.

Right. Let's get started. I suppose you have no idea who might have been responsible?
Well – no, I'm afraid I haven't.

I love it! Typical Jo Public response. Absolutely clueless! What a yum yum!

I take it you're insured?
Oh, yes, Sergeant.
I see.

Well, all I can say is that I hope for your sake it doesn't turn out to be an insurance rip-off. Now, if you would like to remove yourself from the scene of the crime, we'll see what we can do.

Oh, and you won't be leaving the country, will you, Sir? I shall be wanting a statement from you later on, so I'd make sure your story hangs together. All right?

But, but...Sergeant, I haven't done anything wrong!
Hopefully not, Sir; hopefully not.

I don't think I like your attitude.
What did I say, Malc..?
I didn't hear you say anything, Sarge.

Right. So if you wouldn't mind, Sir – I'm sure you must have other things to do.

Durkin goes across to the safe and squats beside it.

"This might seem a silly question," says Malc.

"Then don't ask it!" snarls Durkin.

"But I am here to learn," says Malc.

"All right then, big mouth! So what d'you wanna know?"

"What did you close the safe for, Sarge?"

"I didn't – it slipped."

"Oh." Malc nods. A grin spreads across his face. " It won't be much use as evidence, will it? Not now that it's got your finger prints all over it."

“Listen, Smartypants!” Durkin takes Malc by the tie.

“Just explain to me, Master Clever Detective Constable, how you ever supposed this safe would be any use as evidence? It’s not very likely, is it, that a class villain is going to leave his dabs all over the place?”

“Well, n-no,” says Malc, “but I just thought –”

“It is not up to you to think. Thinking is bad for the brain. Do I make myself clear?”

“Yes, Sarge.”

“Right! Get chummy back in here and tell him to open that safe. And tell him to make it quick or he’s in trouble!”

What? You use coins?
That's original ...
BROOM
CUPBOARD

Chapter 4
Prime Suspect

Maybe so, Clive. But perhaps we'd better not mention this report to the Super for the time being. He's already quite upset enough as it is – what with people putting French francs in the vending machine.
They never!

I'm sad to say that they do, Clive.
Diabolical!

So what am I to tell the Super?
You could say that we are pursuing certain avenues of investigation.

I've already told him that one, Clive.
Honestly, Ma'am, we're nearing a breakthrough. As it happens, I have a suspect waiting for me downstairs at this very moment.

"Oh, well, that's something." Ma'am shakes out her knitting. "Who is he? Do I know him?"

"I don't think so, Ma'am. He's very rough trade. His name's Morris Pratt, and a right prat he is, too."

"Well, you go and have a nice chat with him and see what he can tell you. Let's just hope he feels in a talking mood."

"He will, Ma'am. Don't you worry!"

Clive is interviewing a suspect right now.
I hope he isn't being too energetic...

Chapter 5
Nicely Does It!

Detective Sergeant Durkin is interviewing his suspect. Malc stands by the door, trying to look mean and cool.

"Why don't you do yourself a favour?" says Durkin. "Just tell us where you've stashed the safe and maybe we'll be able to reach an agreement."

Durkin is disgusted. "Don't you give me that! Puny little git. Look at you! Look at the state of you! You couldn't do a decent day's work if you tried. You are living proof of all that's wrong with this society."

Now, you just listen to me, sunshine –
My name's not Sunshine, it's Smith!

What? I thought you were Morris Pratt?
Well, I'm not. I'm Kevin Smith.

?

Malc! Come over here.
What does that say?
Kevin Smith, Sarge.
Kevin Smith,
Can't even write his own name properly. Get him out of here! Chuck him out with the rubbish! And you –
Just watch your step! If I catch you in here again, there will be trouble. I'll have you up for obstructing the course of justice. I'll have you up for wasting police time. I'll have your guts for garters. Now go!

Maybe I was a bit too hasty, Malc. I should have kept him there. Another couple of hours and I'd have broken him...
But he wasn't guilty, Sarge. He hadn't done anything.
AUTO-DRINK

Don't you believe it! They've always done something. There's no such thing as an innocent member of the public.

Knit one, purl one, knit two together...Another safe went missing again last night, you know, Clive. That's two in two days – one from Doggett Road and one from the High Street. It's really not good enough. The Chief is becoming very agitated. What am I supposed to tell him this time?
I can crack the case, Ma'am, I know I can! Just as soon as I lay my hands on Morris Pratt.
Talking of laying hands on people, Clive, I have had a complaint that you insulted an innocent member of the public.
Innocent member of the public!

“Well, Clive?” Ma’am is winding her knitting round her neck. Trying it on for size. “What have you to say for yourself?”

“I thought he was Morris Pratt,” mumbles Durkin.

“Even so –” Ma’am gets up to look at herself in the mirror. Blue and white stripes, O’Grady-the-Grass will like that: he is a Chelsea fan. “Even so, Clive, there is such a thing as asking nicely.”

“Yes, Ma’am.” Durkin is plainly not convinced.

“You don’t have to be unpleasant to people.”

“No, Ma’am.” Durkin is even less convinced.

Ma’am sits down again and unwinds her knitting.

“So when do you think you might be able to locate this Mr Pratt?”

“Any minute now, Ma’am.”

“Very well, then. Off you go! And just remember ...ask nicely!”

Morris, I am asking you nicely!

That's the way to treat 'em, Malc! None of this soft touch rubbish.
He certainly sang, Sarge. 14 Arden Road. Do you reckon they'll still be there?
INTERVIEW ROOM 1

Only one way to find out...let's go and see!

Chapter 6
Unexpected Visitors

14

HOME NEWS
VICAR QUESTIONED IN NIGHT-TIME RAID
REPORTER
CLERICAL SENSATION!
THE GLOB
VICAR ATE MY HAMSTER!
DAILY NEWS
DIANA TO MARRY SWOOP VICAR!
That was the vicar's house that you broke into yesterday, Clive. The Super's very upset.

Next time I lay hands on that Morris...
DO
FOREIGN
THIS

Meanwhile, it's business as usual for Sergeant Slocum.

Sergeant Durkin?
Speaking.

If you're looking for the safe from the Doggett Road blag, you'll find it buried in the field at the Ladywell Rec.

Hello? Who is this? Hello?

Hello? Hello?

Ladywell Rec! On the double!

GROAN!
GRUNT!!
Must weigh a ton!
Nearly there, Sarge!

Get a light on it, get a light on it!

PROPERTY OF BRITISH TELECOM
JUNCTION BOX
EVER BEEN HAD?

Chapter 7
Stake Out

Yes, and it led you to uproot a British Telecom junction box! Half the telephones in Catford have gone down! The villains are having a field day! I don't know what we're going to do with you, Clive, I really don't.

Just give me one more chance, Ma'am! That's all I ask.
It's all you'll get. Heads are going to roll for this, you know, Clive!

Heads are going to roll for this, you know, Malc. And one of 'em ain't gonna be mine!

Phone Sarge...says its a tip off...

So you reckon you're really on to something this time Sarge?
Listen, Malc, I've got a reputation. I'm a hard man. No one gives Clive Durkin the run-around more than once.

Twice, actually, Sarge.
Did I hear you say something, Malc?
Not me, Sarge.

M.R. SMALL JEWELLER
EST 1925

Red Leader to Bert. Come in, Bert.

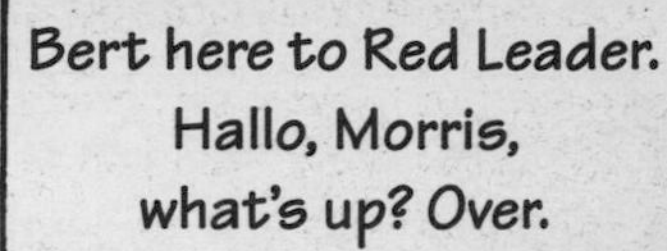
Bert here to Red Leader. Hallo, Morris, what's up? Over.

Having a wonderful time, wish you was here. What's Durkin-the-Gherkin up to?

Still watching the jeweller's shop down the road, the stupid berk!

Inside the squad car. One hour later.

JEWELLER
POLICE

That way, Sarge!
They went that way!

WAH! WAH! WAH!
POLICE
SCREECH

Chapter 8
Daylight Robbery

It is two days later. Wally has come to have his usual eleven o'clock cuppa with Phyllis.

"Shall I be mother?" says Ma'am. She puts down her knitting and picks up the coffee pot.

"Please," says Wally. "You know, Phyllis, I really think I shall have to recommend Detective Sergeant Durkin for a promotion. It was perfectly splendid the way he cracked those safe robberies!"

"Yes, wasn't it?" agrees Ma'am. "I told you he was a good lad."

"And it's stopped the Commissioner barking at me, thank heavens! Mind you..." Wally sits forward, his forehead crinkling. "I'm still very concerned about all those French francs being put into the coffee machine."

Ma'am picks up her knitting needles and begins to cast on stitches.

"Don't you worry. I'll get Clive on to it."

We gotta do something to stop all these French francs being put in here, Malc. We'll have to organise a stake-out...
AUTO-DRINKS
COFFEE
COFFEE

I mean, let's face it Malc, it's just another form of robbery...